Mr. Bumbleticker's Apples

Written by Sandra Iversen ● Illustrated by Peter Paul Bajer

Gus is at the bus stop.
He is going to school.
Mr. Bumbleticker is in his truck.
He is going to the market.
He is going to sell his apples
at the market.

2

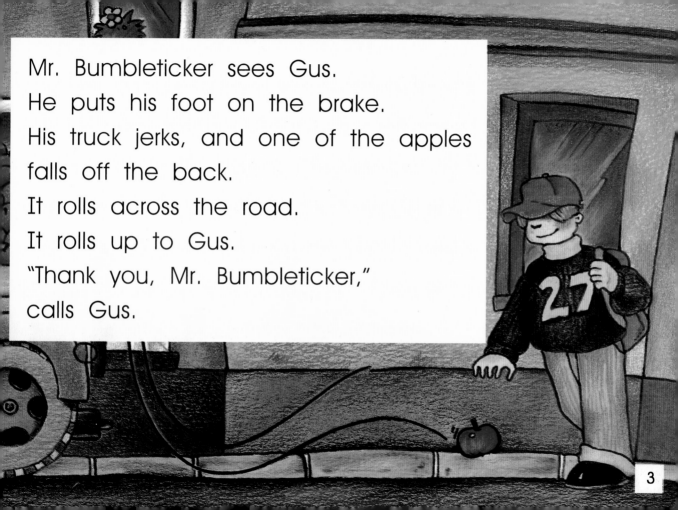

Mr. Bumbleticker sees Gus.

He puts his foot on the brake.

His truck jerks, and one of the apples falls off the back.

It rolls across the road.

It rolls up to Gus.

"Thank you, Mr. Bumbleticker," calls Gus.

3

Mandy and Kate are going to school.
"Here comes Mr. Bumbleticker,"
says Mandy.
"He is going to the market.
He is going to sell his apples."

5

Mr. Bumbleticker sees Mandy and Kate.
He puts his foot on the brake.
His truck jerks, and two apples
fall off the back.
They roll across the road.
They roll up to Mandy and Kate.
"Thank you, Mr. Bumbleticker,"
call Mandy and Kate.

Rick and Molly and Tim
are at the school gate.
Mr. Bumbleticker drives by.
Rick calls out to Mr. Bumbleticker.
"Hello, Mr. Bumbleticker.
Are you going to the market
to sell your apples?"

8

9

Mr. Bumbleticker stops his truck.
"I think I will give all my apples
to the children today,"
he says.
Mr. Bumbleticker drives his truck
into the school yard.

He puts his foot on the brake,
and lots of apples fall off.
"Come and get an apple,
come and get an apple,"
calls Mr. Bumbleticker.

The teacher and the children
come to get the apples.
"You are a kind man, Mr. Bumbleticker,"
says the teacher.
"You are kind to come to the school
and give your apples to the children."

13

"Thank you, Mr. Bumbleticker,"
say the children.
"Thank you for bringing us the apples.
We like apples."

Mr. Bumbleticker drives away in his truck.
He drives home.
"We must pick some more apples,"
he says to Mrs. Bumbleticker.
"We must pick some more apples
to take to the market."

"Today I gave all our apples
to the children."

"That was a good thing to do,"
said Mrs. Bumbleticker.
"You are a kind man, Mr. Bumbleticker."

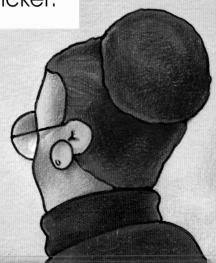